CW00348949

Playalong for Saxophone
SPORTING THEMES

Wise Publications
part of The Music Sales Group
LONDON / NEW YORK / PARIS / SYDNEY / COPENHAGEN / BERLIN / MADRID / HONG KONG / TOKYO

Published by
Wise Publications
14-15 Berners Street, London W1T 3LJ, UK.

Exclusive Distributors:
Music Sales Limited
Distribution Centre, Newmarket Road, Bury St Edmunds,
Suffolk IP33 3YB, UK.
Music Sales Pty Limited
20 Resolution Drive, Caringbah, NSW 2229, Australia.

Order No. AM1004762
ISBN 13: 978-1-78038-571-6
This book © Copyright 2012 Wise Publications,
a division of Music Sales Limited.

Edited by Jenni Norey.
Top line arrangements by Christopher Hussey.
Backing tracks programmed by Jeremy Birchall and John Maul.
Music processed by Camden Music Services.
Saxophone played by Howard McGill.
CD recorded, mixed and mastered by Jonas Persson.

Printed in the EU.

Saxophone Fingering Chart

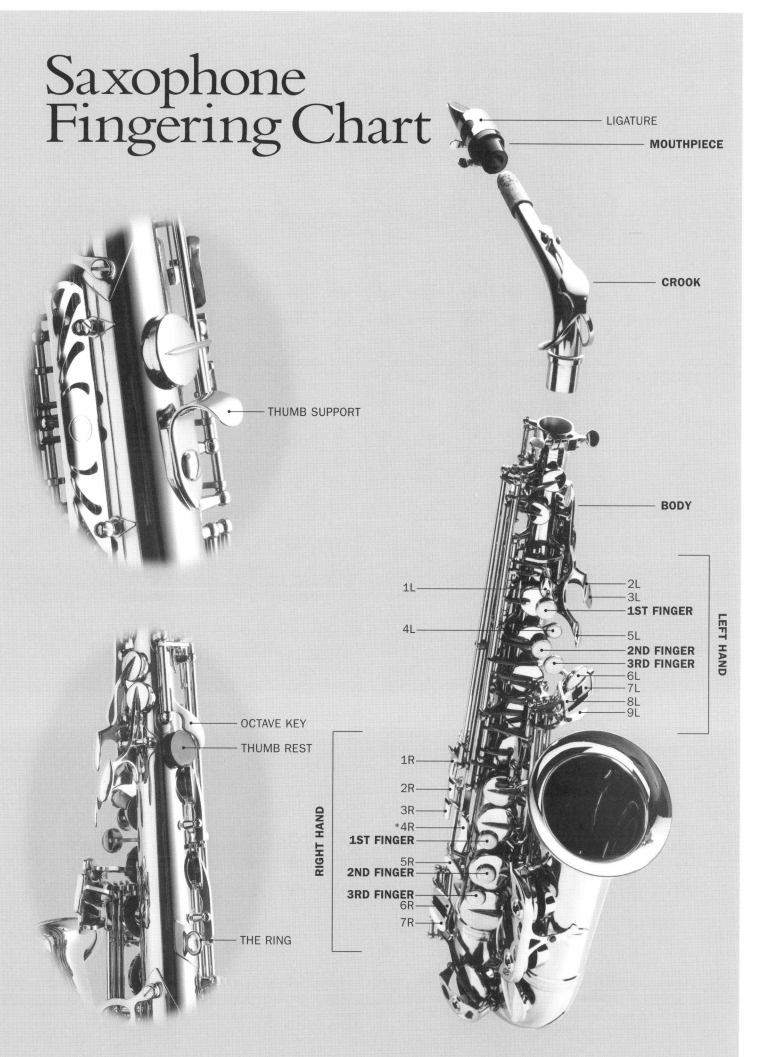

LIGATURE

MOUTHPIECE

CROOK

THUMB SUPPORT

BODY

1L
2L
3L
1ST FINGER
4L
5L
2ND FINGER
3RD FINGER
6L
7L
8L
9L

LEFT HAND

OCTAVE KEY

THUMB REST

1R
2R
3R
*4R
1ST FINGER
5R
2ND FINGER
3RD FINGER
6R
7R

RIGHT HAND

THE RING

* Not fitted on some saxophones

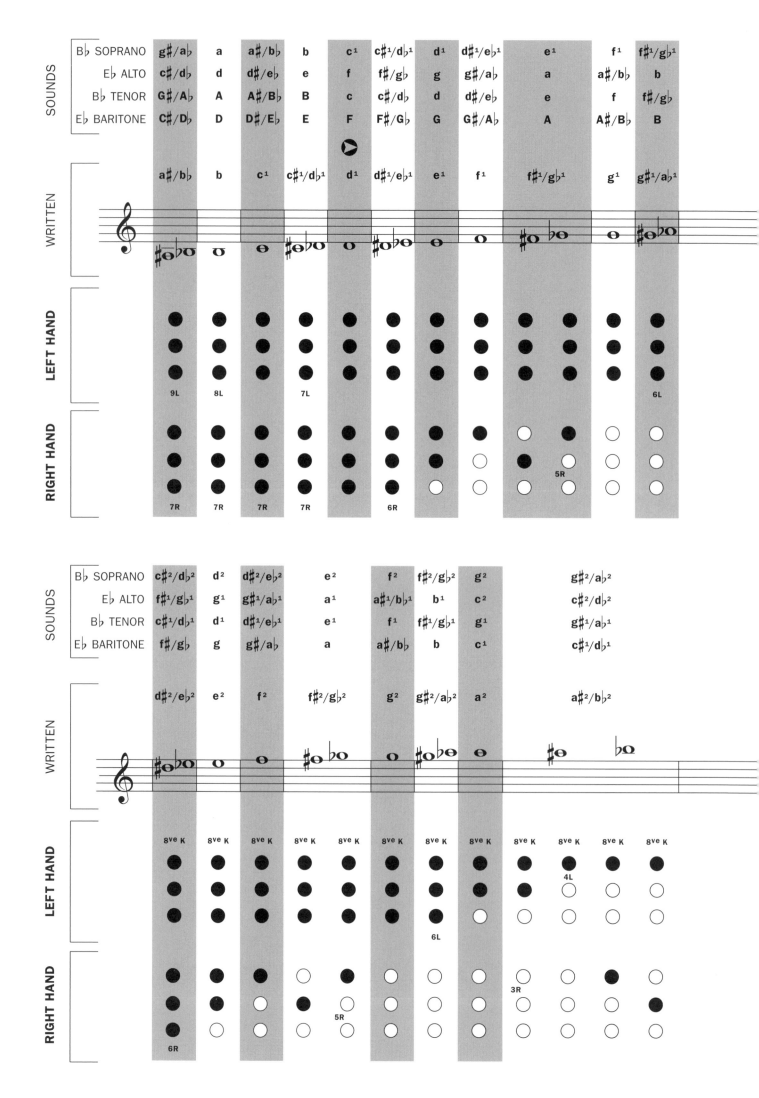

Indicates the lower limit of the best playing range

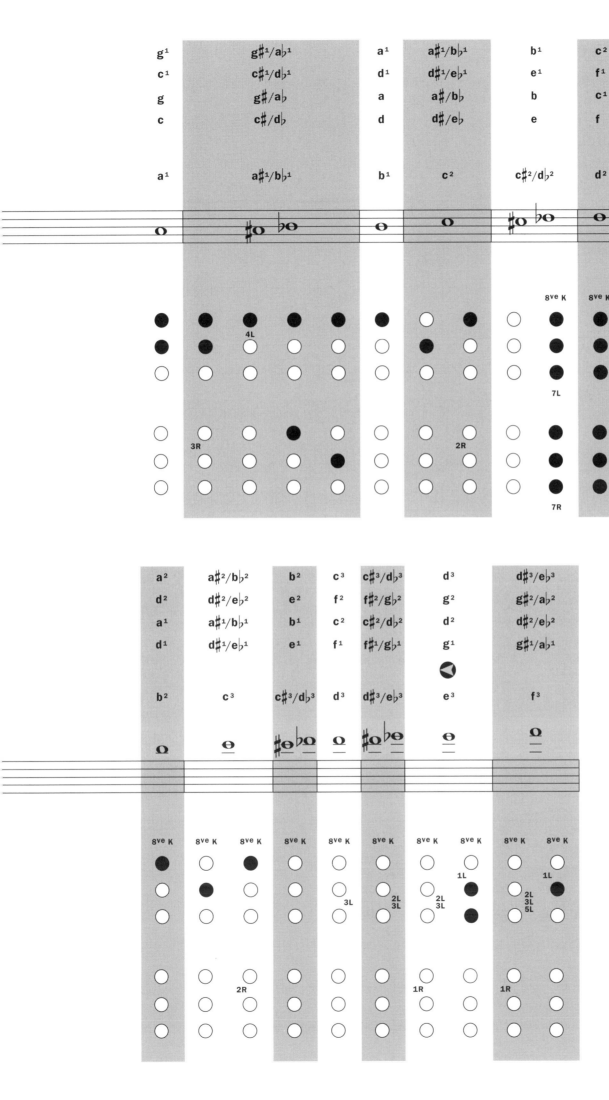

Indicates the upper limit of the best playing range

Grandstand

Music by Keith Mansfield

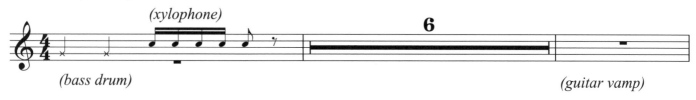

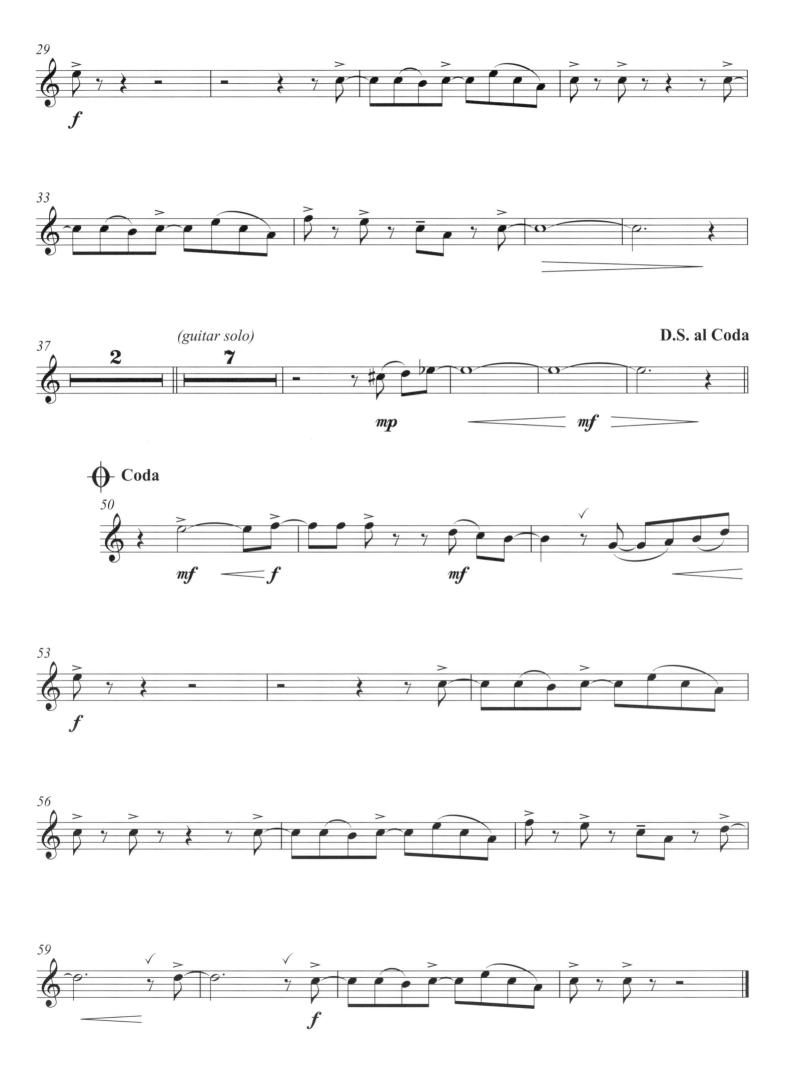

Light And Tuneful (Wimbledon Opening Theme)

Music by Keith Mansfield

With a bounce ♩ = 144

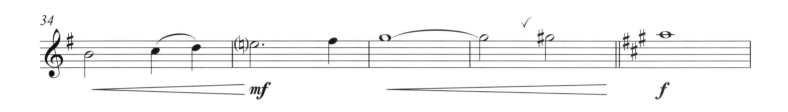

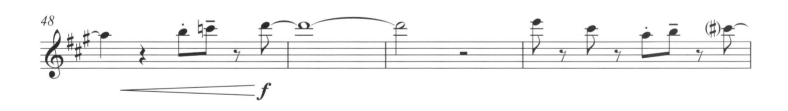

Match Of The Day

Music by Barry Stoller

Lightly ♩ = 112

(whistle)

mf

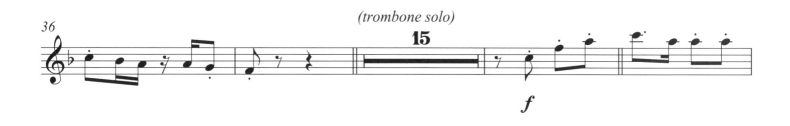

(trombone solo)

15

f

mf

ff

A Musical Joke (BBC Horse Of The Year)

Music by Wolfgang Amadeus Mozart

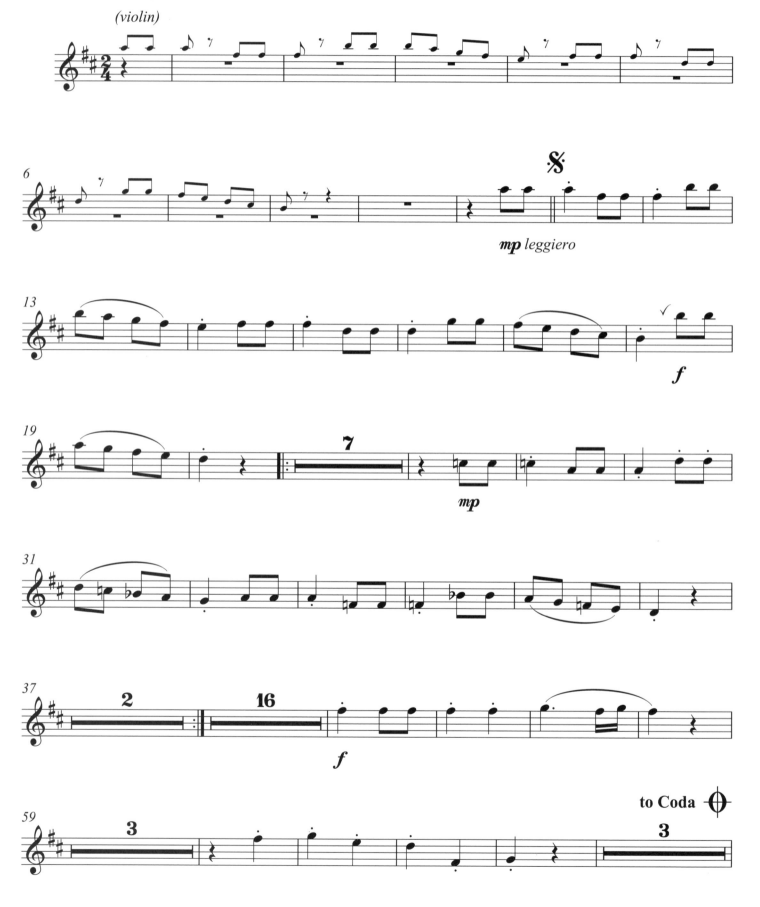

Out Of The Blue (Theme to "Sports Report")

Music by Hubert Bath

Pop Looks Bach (Ski Sunday Theme)

Music by Sam Fonteyn

A Question Of Sport

Music by Richard Close

With a driving rhythm ♩ = 163

1. *(guitar solo)*
2. *(guitar solo)*

D.S. al Coda

(drum break)

Coda

(guitar solo)

mf

f

Soul Limbo (Test Match Special)

Music by Steve Cropper, Booker T. Jones, Al Jackson & Donald 'Duck' Dunn

World In Union (World Cup Rugby 1991)

Music by Gustav Holst arranged by Charlie Skarbek

World Of Sport

Words & Music by Jeff Wayne

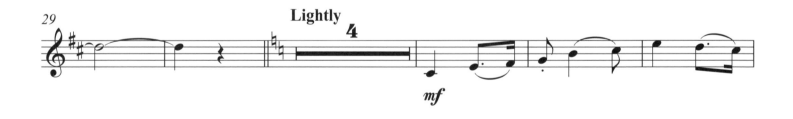

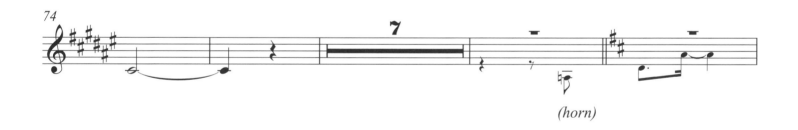

1 2 3 4 5 6 7 8 9

CD Track Listing

Full instrumental performances...

1. Tuning notes

2. Grandstand
   (Mansfield) KPM Music Limited

3. Light And Tuneful
   (Mansfield) KPM Music Limited

4. Match Of The Day
   (Stoller) RAK Publishing Limited

5. A Musical Joke
   (Mozart) Dorsey Brothers Music Limited

6. Out Of The Blue
   (Bath) Copyright Control

7. Pop Looks Bach
   (Fonteyn) Cavendish Music Company Limited

8. A Question Of Sport
   (Close) Richard Close

9. Soul Limbo
   (Cropper/Jones/Jackson/Dunn) Universal Music Publishing Limited

10. World In Union
    (Skarbek/Holst) Standard Music Ltd

11. World Of Sport
    (Wayne) Standard Music Ltd

Backing tracks only...

12. Grandstand

13. Light And Tuneful

14. Match Of The Day

15. A Musical Joke

16. Out Of The Blue

17. Pop Looks Bach

18. A Question Of Sport

19. Soul Limbo

20. World In Union

21. World Of Sport

MCPS

To remove your CD from the plastic sleeve, lift the small lip to break the perforations. Replace the disc after use for convenient storage